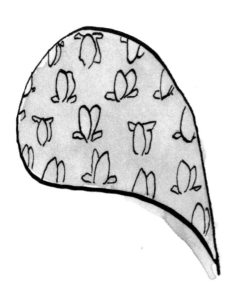

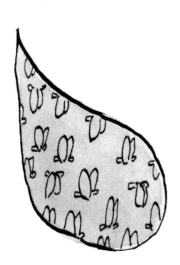

Proper Go Well High

a Trains Are...Mint book
by
Oliver East

Blank Slate, London
2008

Slate 3

Proper Go Well High

copyright © Oliver East 2008

Publishers: James Hamilton, Kenny Penman
Editorial assistant: Isobel Rips
Book Design: Oliver East, Duncan Bullimore

Discover more about Blank Slate at
www.blankslatebooks.co.uk

Thanks doodle

Part 1

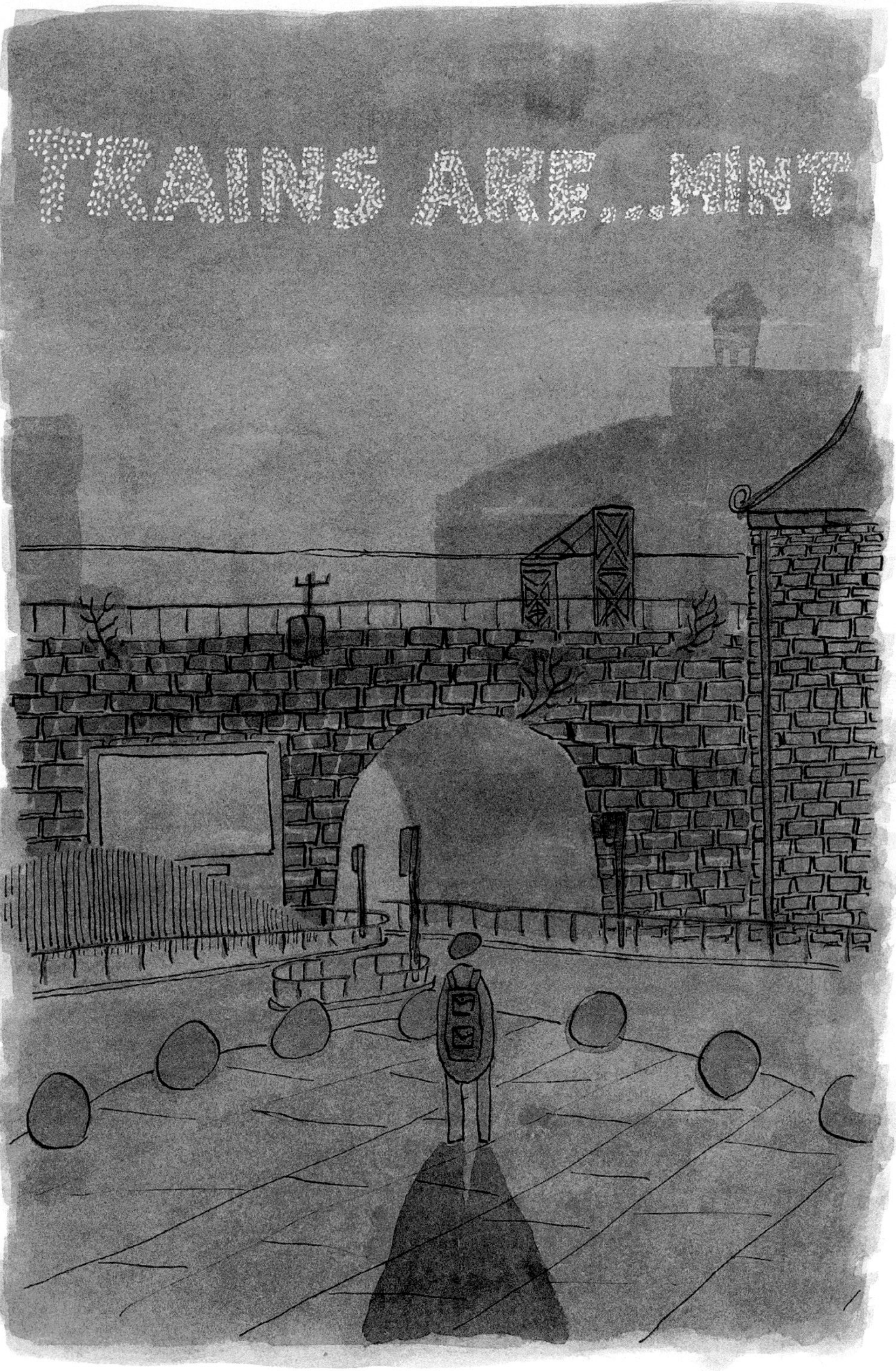
TRAINS ARE...MINT

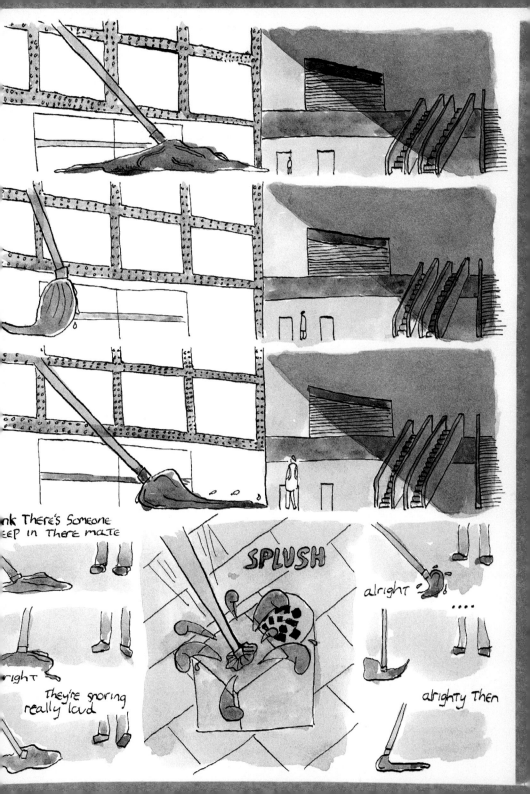

FALL INTO MY BED

Start the walk from under the elevated platforms 13&14, safe in the assumption there's no PROSTITUTES out at this hour so I can walk where I please

Try to keep the tracks to my left as it'll give me an xcuse to draw some of my favourite buildings, such as

MANCHESTER MECHANICS' INSTITUTE

U. M. I. S. T.

vaguely chastise myself for being disappointed that there's no tramps under the arches between Sackville Street and Princess Street.

's a good thing no one's sleeping there.

Good for them.

They would have been nice to draw though.

I feel shame's hand pulling me on.

pulling me on to Oxford Road station

which I wasn't going to bother with as I'm so familiar with it, but I pop in anyway to see its disused platform I've always liked

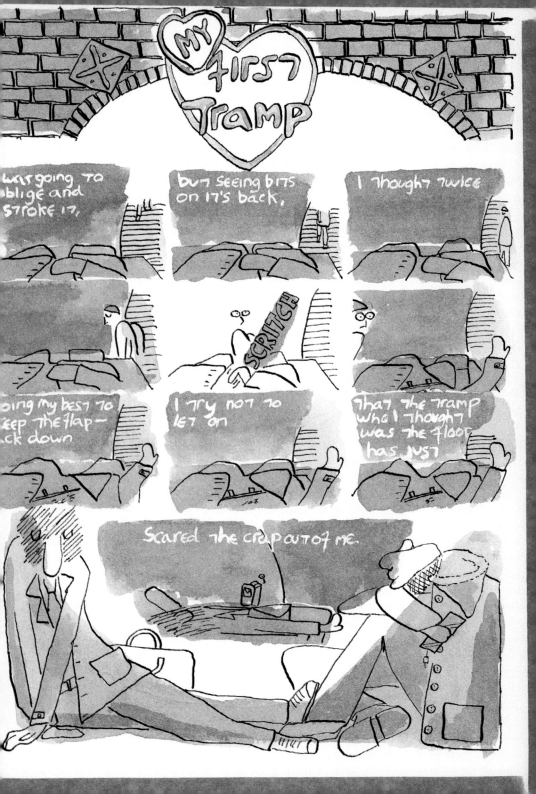

The entrance to Deansgate Station smells like bacon butties this early in the morning.

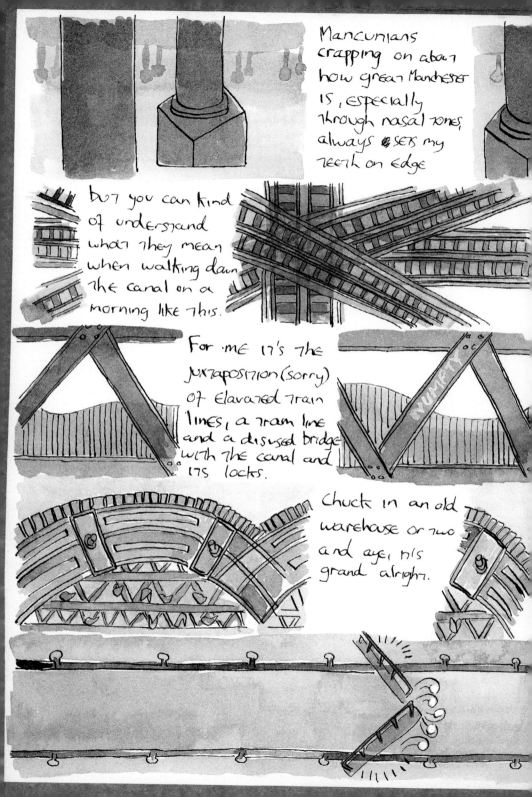

Mancunians crapping on about how great Manchester is, especially through nasal tones, always sets my teeth on edge

but you can kind of understand what they mean when walking down the canal on a morning like this.

For me it's the juxtaposition (sorry) of elevated train lines, a tram line and a disused bridge with the canal and its locks.

Chuck in an old warehouse or two and aye, it's grand alright.

There's no one like canal boat enthusiasts for adhering to STEREOTYPE

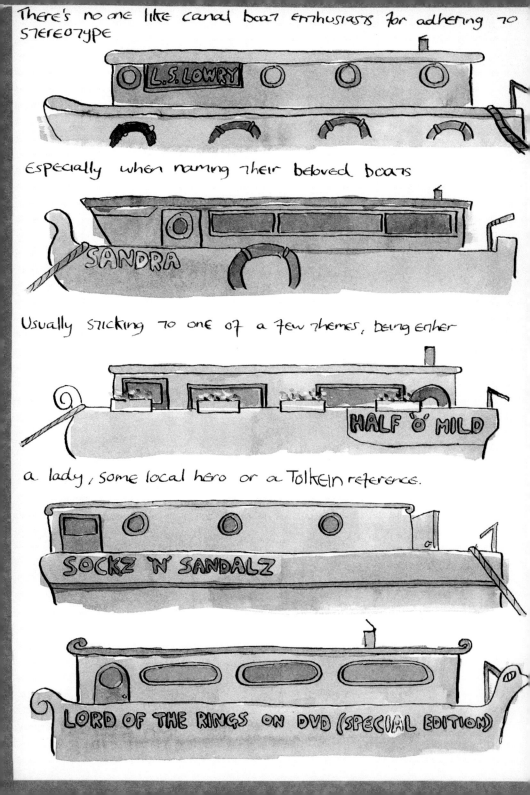

L.S. LOWRY

Especially when naming their beloved boats

SANDRA

Usually sticking to one of a few themes, being either

HALF 'O' MILD

a lady, some local hero or a Tolkein reference.

SOCKZ 'N' SANDALZ

LORD OF THE RINGS ON DVD (SPECIAL EDITION)

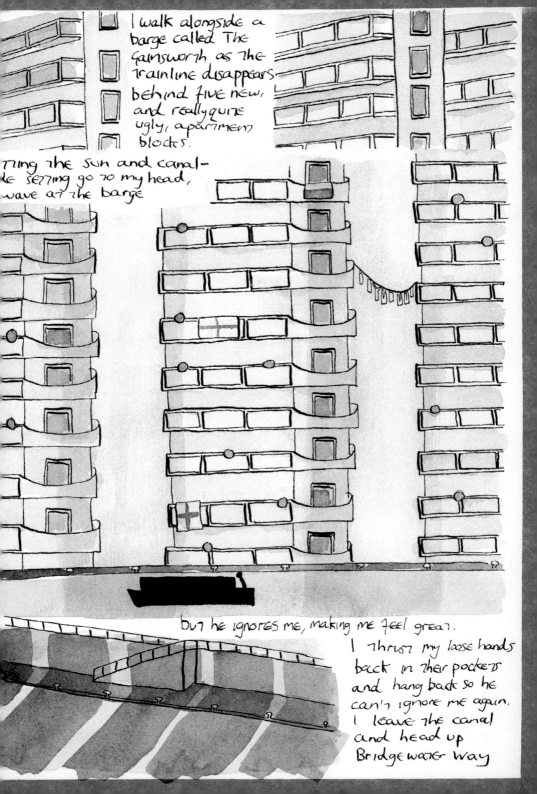

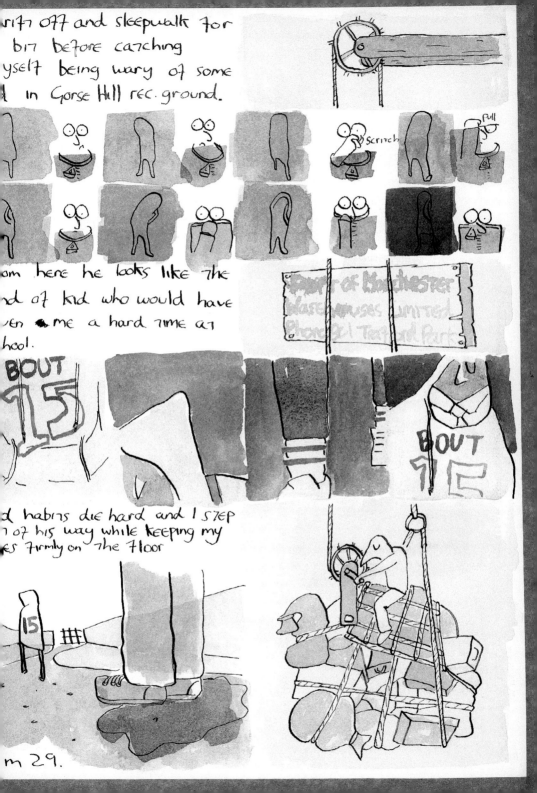

...rift off and sleepwalk for a bit before catching myself being wary of some[thing] in Gorse Hill rec. ground.

...om here he looks like the [ki]nd of kid who would have [gi]ven me a hard time at [sc]hool.

[Ol]d habits die hard and I step [out] of his way while keeping my [ey]es firmly on the floor

Scritch

Pull

BOUT 15

BOUT 15

15

...m 29.

Regeneration might have given everyone fancy double glazing but there's not much difference from STREET to STREET in Trafford

The northern line to Liverpool's got all the history, being the world's passenger line, but the southern's got more stations which is why I'm walking this one. I might walk the northern route back.

L'POOL

MCR

Wahey luv!

TOOLS

BEEP BEEP

BAG O PHONES

15

HD

PLAGA

CC

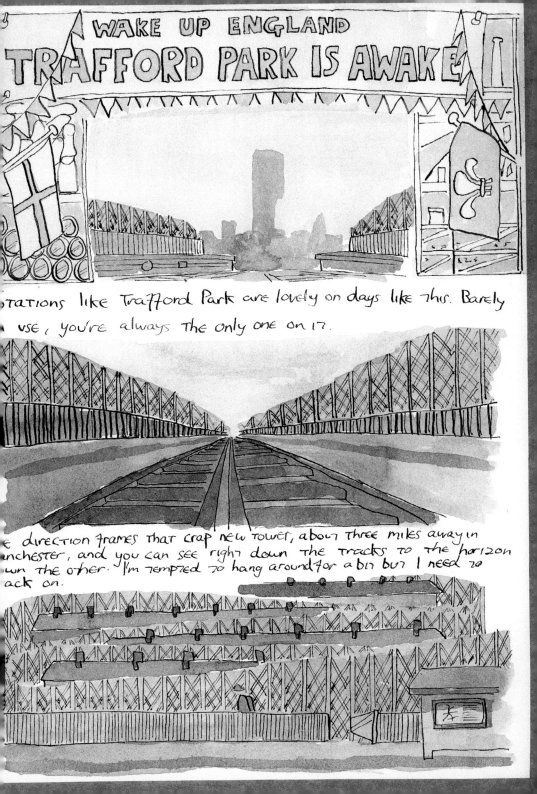

WAKE UP ENGLAND
TRAFFORD PARK IS AWAKE

Stations like Trafford Park are lovely on days like this. Barely
use, you're always the only one on it.

...e direction frames that crap new tower, about three miles away in
...nchester, and you can see right down the tracks to the horizon
...wn the other. I'm tempted to hang around for a bit but I need to
...ack on.

Humphrey Park station was a welcome break from the council estates of Stretford, as it was pink! How good's that?

You don't get many pink stations and I envy those whose houses back onto this little bit of holiday camp.

I make a note to check what hill I can see on the horizon at the end of the tracks, but I never did.

TWAT ON A PHONE

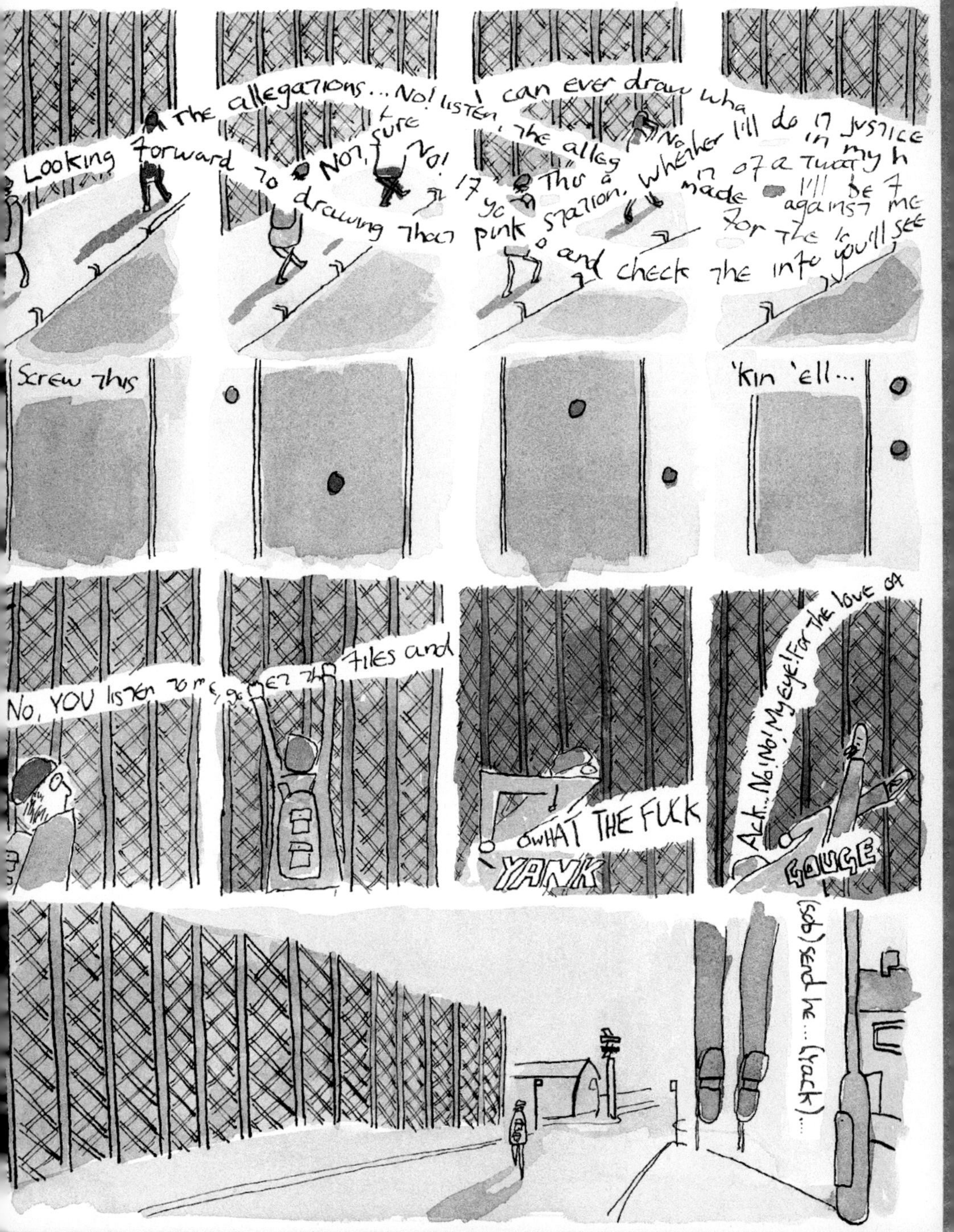

combination of tattooed hands, a toothless lisp and
bout a foot on me mean I don't get to hang
round at Urmston Station. Shame, really, because it
ooked alright and getting beaten up would've
iven good copy.

ut I like my face where it
Thanks

I find a narrow path
leading to Chasson Road
Station

hich has a miniature railway
the park ~~effort~~ opposite

But with no place to sit I
leave, looking forward to
drawing the miniature railway

t feeling bad for not waving at that passing train driver

A long footpath running between two golf courses allows me time to think, and subsequently worry about, how the hell you draw a long footpath running between two golf courses.

Trying not to worry about it is a fruitless exercise, knowing full well it'll bug me till I tackle it.

Oh well.

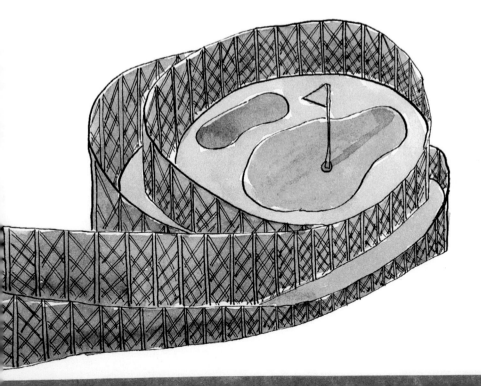

It's just a short phone call,

about where's best to leave a shepherd's pie to defrost without the cats getting to it, before

before getting to

u tell some people you do omics and they ve you a look

It's like you've JUST Told Them you've got AIDS, like," oh dear, well, we're here if you need us!"

Or you've just done a nasty hangover fart, like, "Oh really, did you have to."

I'd be lying if I said it didn't matter what people thought.

r when I die and they find a load of unsold books under my d, and I'm recognised as the genius of the form I was

hen you'll see

YOU'LL ALL SEE

Hello Mr East? This is sexy lady journalist from (insert quality Sunday paper), may I talk to you about your new book?

Why yes, sexy lady journalis as long as you don't mind bei on speaker phone. You see I'm drawing and talking at the sam Time.

Wow, Multitasking! You are brilliant!

Well, I don't know about that, but yes. Yes I am.

So what's this next winner about?

I'm walking from Manchester to Lverpoo might walk back but I'll see how this first stretch goes first.

Sounds like another b to me. After the first bo won all them awards a girls and that, is there any pressure to make th next one killer from cov to cover?

Well Miranda, may I call you Miranda?

. . . .

Well Miranda, the answer's yes and no. Mainly yes though. Not much no really.

Have I morphed into Miranda Sawyer in this sad little fantasy of yours?

Sorry Miranda, can you just hold on f a second?

Big Ditch

1d   2d

2d

After the impressive Irlam locks   Irlam Station's not up to much   There's a 'Friends of Irlam Station Society'   but I can't see what good they're doing

There being no seats provided, I sit amongst some broken glass and eat my cheese.

I thought this'd be as far as I'd get today, but I brought my Warrington A to Z just in case, so I'm going to press on. It's only 11.45.

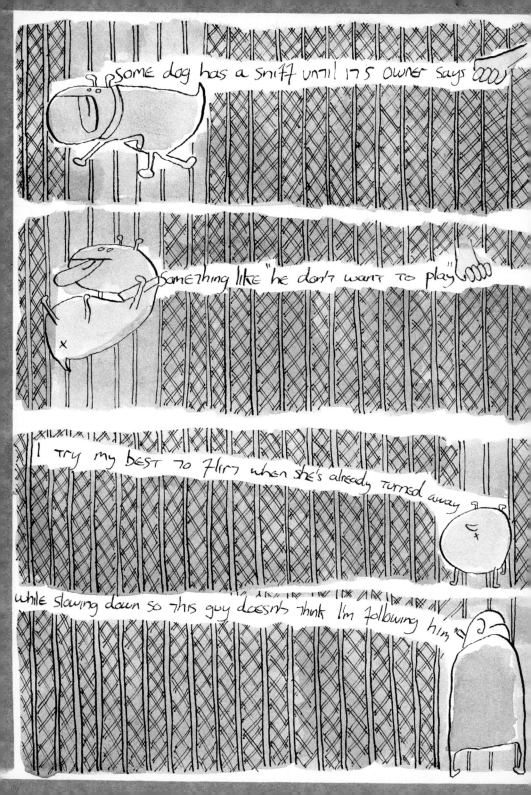

n not convinced this dirt road's   or if I'm Trespassing or not
n my map

o I'm pretty chuffed when the path comes parallel with
he Tracks with no fence between us.

ren though it turns out to be a dead end, it's well worth it.

y heart sinks, only a bit but noticeably so, as I descend into nother IDENTIKIT suburban ESTATE

ut after I see some old lady point out two swans to er dog, I notice, maybe not a spring as such, but I'm efinitely walking tall. I might be smiling as well but onh tell anyone.

cause of my early start this morning, I went without a ower which means I'm pretty greasy now plus I think I might e getting sunburnt. Civilisation's thinning out now though I can be as sweaty as I like on my own.

s becoming less fun now.

I might not be limping yet but I'm feeling it in my feet

o I'm glad when Glazebrook ation turns up.

No, tell a lie, I'm knackered but good knackered.

e achieved something of sorts. nall victories, that's what it's bout.

With no train home for another two hours, I suck it up and press on to the next station!

Huya mate, what time's next Manchester Train?

Cheers mate

FIVE MINUTES

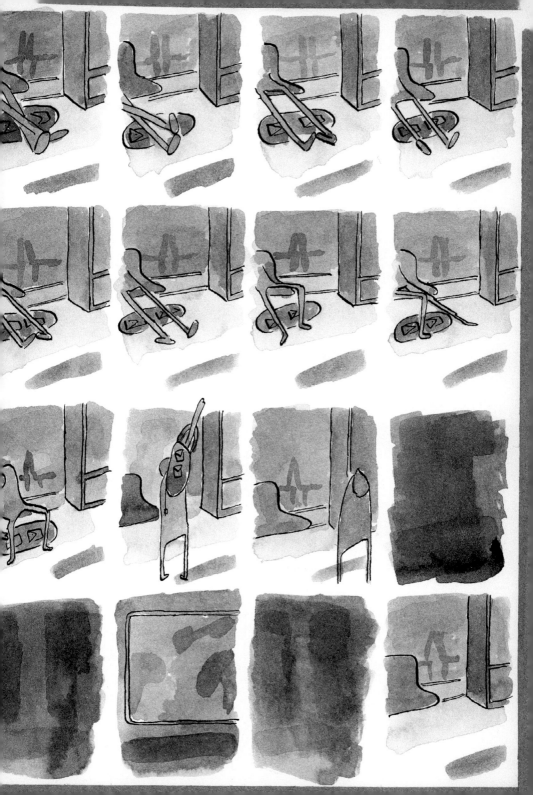

Part 2

year and a
17 has passed
ce the first
17 of this walk

I'm still just about
my ideal weight

But my hair's a
little less impressive

And I've seen
more of China
and Japan than
I had.

hat is to say
ve been

I'm also a best
friend lighter

But we'll not go
there

I got to a point
here I couldn't
o any more
rawing without
ome more
walking

So I'm back on
Birchwood Station
at 6.57am

Last time I was
here I was a
sorry state, all
knackered and
shiny

Fingers crossed
we'll get there
again

I'm trying for
Liverpool today.
That's twelve
stations worth

I just tried to
write the excited
noise I just made

But the best I
could come up
with is:
WARHORHOR!

It's a good
noise.

last time round here I was in danger of getting sunburnt

Now, on February 1st, a touch of snow greets me as I leave Birchwood Station with the tune of some sweary bloke in my ear.

I think I'll have more fun drawing wind than rain

But it's been so long, I've forgotten how to write with my gloves on.

knew I'd enjoy it more if I came out when it's oper cold and windy. More of a challenge and makes or better copy.

zying that though, it's just rar7ed raining in my face

And I've not figured ou7 how I draw rain ye7.

I STEEL myself before
Tackling a rapey
looking path

...nd after about, ooh, all of
...en minutes I'm lost

...and the whole violent-sexual-attack-vibe of the place is nicely topped off by a faulty lamp.

A road sign would be nice about mnow.

AND BEFORE YOU
KNOW IT
I FIND ONE
WA3

but before I can check my map

my own shadow scares the crap out of me.

Screw it, I'm just going to go this way and see what happens

IT'S on Warrington Road where things get a little less rapey
I finally figure out where I am and where I'm supposed to be
IT'S a bigger detour than I'd planned but at least I'm back on track
Kinsdale Drive? No? Hold on. No, right... that's the one I was on

IT'S GETTING lighter now but looks like there'll still be grey skies later.

Grey skies make for better drawings

I prefer them to the blue of the first stretch.

LOCKING STUMPS LANE! WHAT A GREAT NAME! WA3

I'd like to tell you ITS meaning but I've still not kicked my Friends habit

This is the first bit since setting off that I'm actually walking towards Liverpool. After an hour and a half.

Hey, a golf course!

It's warm enough to write without my gloves on now

But there really is too muc blue to ignore

I have a proper big sigh while passing some 'bird's nest.

Nothing to do with the nest. I just forgot how much I lov these walks.

Going by the school run, I'm guessing it's just gone 8.

Although I can't be sure having got rid of my phone.

Padgate Station looks good from here. Here being the path approaching it because I don't want the people on the opposite platform to see me writing.

I pretend to look at train times with one eye

while making mental notes on the Station Houses architecture with the other.

Of course I write that last bit on the path leaving the station

DAILY ⊕ EVENT

#9,388

...n I get a ...ttle of water ...ease?	Can. I. get. a. bottle. of. water. Thanks?	Bottle of water please.	Bottle. Bottle of water thanks.

...ust this	Just this thanks	(phump?)	Bottle of...

...just this thanks	Just this thanks	....	Just. this. thanks.

..., thanks	Hi	Hi	....

BREAD CAFE NEWS & WATER HERE GOES

There's a little queue inside so I dordle outside for a secon

New quad bike
Push button start
£995 ONO

£60 Solid Pine b/room
furniture 2 x Chinese
vase with wooden
rose stand
555-4987

2 x Suitcase in silver
with security code +
Groovy chick blue
Furry seat £60

SPOT CASH
(Up to £1000) Punto, Escorts & Vans Etc.
• M.O.T Failures • Damaged Term
• FREE REMOVAL
24HRS - 7days Prompt, Polite Service
0161 737 1582 / 07908 413 413 (Direct)
EAN 947100 **OLLY MOTORS**

Carol
Ironing
Service
Pick up or
pop in
(over Sainsburys

Wealthy Wednesdays

See website for full Terms and

I've gone the wrong way, Balls. Well, I'll enjoy drawing those smoking girls.

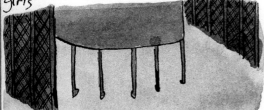

But twenty minutes the wrong way is still twenty minutes the wrong way.

And I wouldn't have seen those cards in the newsagent's window

All of a sudden the rain isn't as much fun anymore.

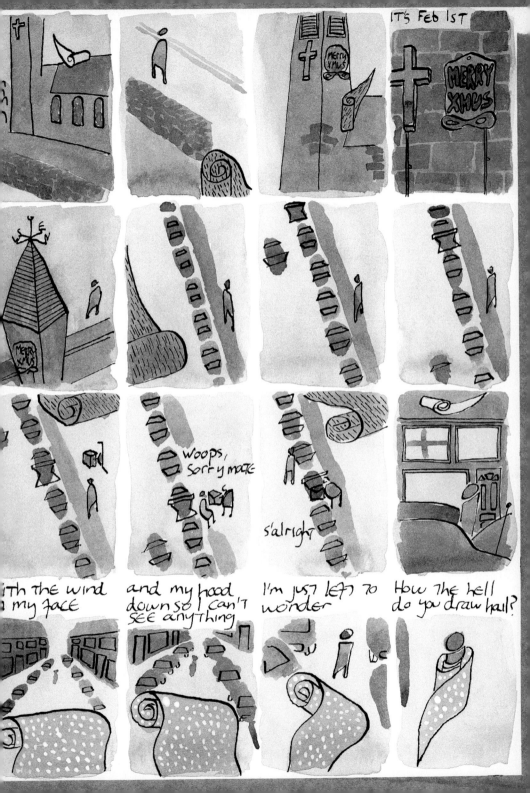

I lose my bearings trying to get pen off my good coat so I just head for the nearest main road.

where An impressive church tower tells me it's half nine but I find it hard to believe it's been two and a half hours already.

After crossing some roundabout my mind wanders as I walk the long, beige approach to Warrington Central Station.

Upon reaching Warrington Central Station I'm desperate for seat and my sandwich, with pork and pistachio being a rather leftfield choice.

It turns out the church was right as well, it's 9.48 no three hours it's taken me to get here.

That's not even half way, leaving Liverpool in a day in da

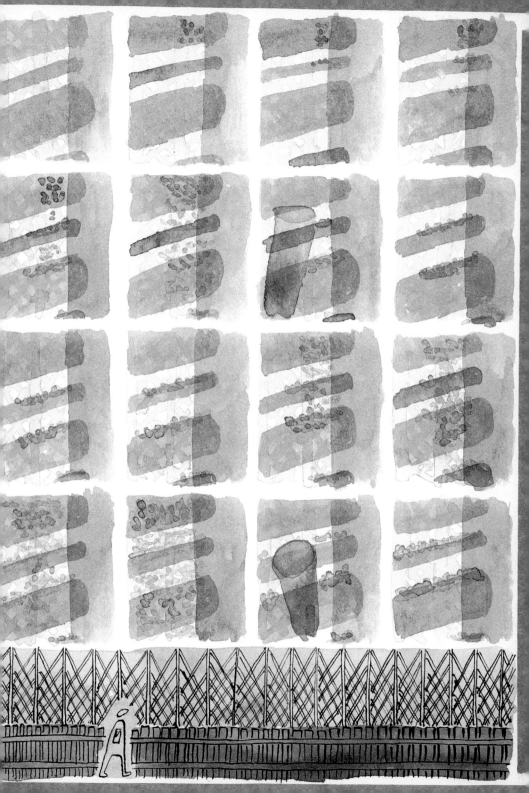

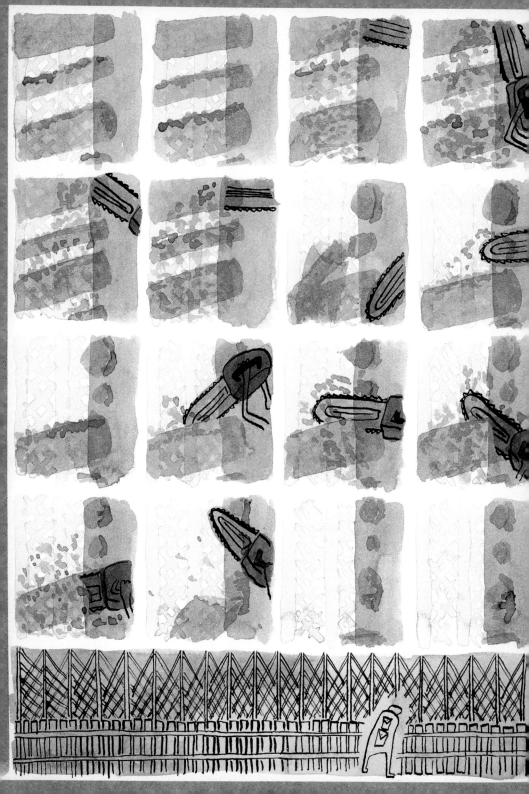

here's a church, Mary's, and again swear 17's clock's wrong

There's no way 17's Ten past two. Four hours since Warrington?

Nope, not having 17.

BRITISH
LEGION

SANKEY AND PENKETH CONCERT...

"This Friday by popular demand, All Round Star Alan Street"

and "Billy Rivers, Great Guitar Vocalist".

This bus stop says the next bus is at 11.47. I knew I was rig

WARRINGTON 12 mins

SANKEY AND PENKETH CON

THE Sun's doing that thing where it's Shining
Through the clouds as if God's Scanning his work
to show people for possible future commissions.

Apparently Sunnybank is supported by Widnes Soroptimists

I'd go down and have a look maybe find out what the hell a Soroptimist is.

BEST FOR WOMEN

But my legs are proper knackered and I want to crack on to Widnes,

The footpath on my map, at the end of Bishop's Way, is no where to be seen.

But it ends at a playing field called The Bongs.

Where I'm mildy harrassed by an over excited puppy before crossing Bower's Brook.

eally want to make Liverpool today

I'm close to six hours in and not even in the Liverpool AtoZ yet.

feeling it now. See how I go.

Widnes' graffiti
fails at
the first
hitting.

IT'S all
cocks
This

FANNY
THAT

and
Becky's
a
crack
baby

...EST some well knackered
...ys in Widnes' graffiti-less
...elter. Its station house is
...etty much the same as the
...evious two, but it's got a
...milar bridge to Flixton's.
...scinating I know.

A combination of me not wanting this thing to become just an endurance test, and there being a train home in five minutes mean I call it a day.

...could crack on but it would
...come less about the walk
...nd more about how many
...sters I can deal with. I'm
...sappointed not to have reached
...erpool but it turns out that
...dnes is in the Liverpool AtoZ.

Anyway, the skies are turning blue and I don't like drawing blue skies.

PLATFORM

Part 3

The 6.24, the first train of the day, stopped at every stop on the way back to Widnes, which was good to see how far I've come.

Helped me get excited again especially when I feel like I've been punched in the face. I'm pretty tired.

Because it's June, it's as light at 6.24 as it's going to get all day

So I could've had a lie in, started a bit later and you'd have been none the wiser.

But that'd be cheating. It would be nice if it were a bit brighter though.

Give my sunglasses an excuse to hide these bags.

ght at the start my watch loses its time. No matter, I
ckon I can make liverpool today. My train got in at
venish I think.

I footpath opens up onto a
assive playing field with no
sible path to follow.

Could be trespassing here, not sure.
There's some thick grey clouds
ahead as well. Could pour down.

m always slightly disappointed in myself when I start these things
ired and hungover, like I might not do a good job. But
ometimes it's the best mood for it; stumbling along some
rain line till your feet hurt and you go home. Mint.

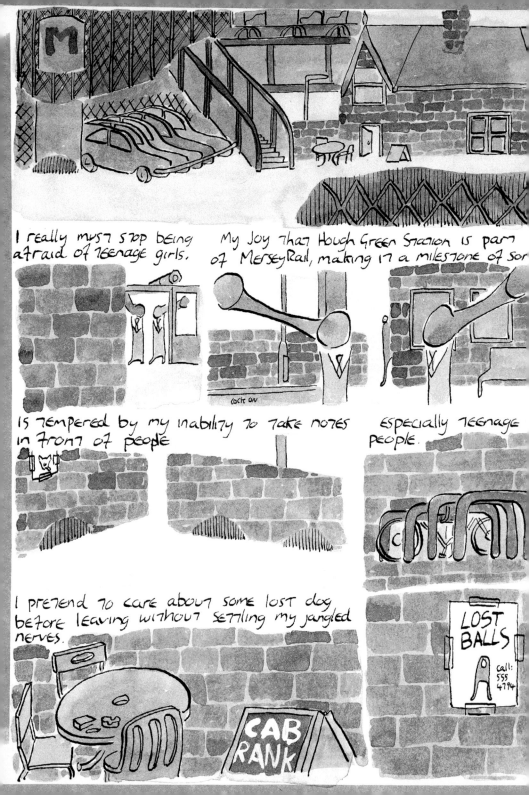

I really must stop being afraid of teenage girls.

My joy that Hough Green Station is part of MerseyRail, making it a milestone of sor[...]

cock on

is tempered by my inability to take notes in front of people

especially teenage people.

I pretend to care about some lost dog before leaving without settling my jangled nerves.

CAB RANK

LOST BALLS
call: 555 4794

I try smiling again but a reflection means I can't tell if they smiled back. I'm guessing not.

I do a proper cheesy grin and stop just short of high fiving myself as

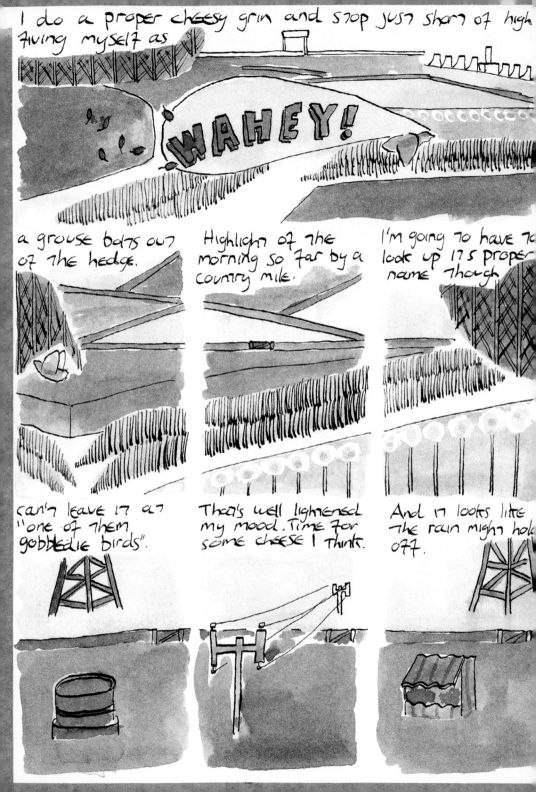

WAHEY!

a grouse bolts out of the hedge.

Highlight of the morning so far by a country mile.

I'm going to have to look up its proper name though

can't leave it at "one of them gobbledie birds".

That's well lightened my mood. Time for some cheese I think.

And it looks like the rain might hold off.

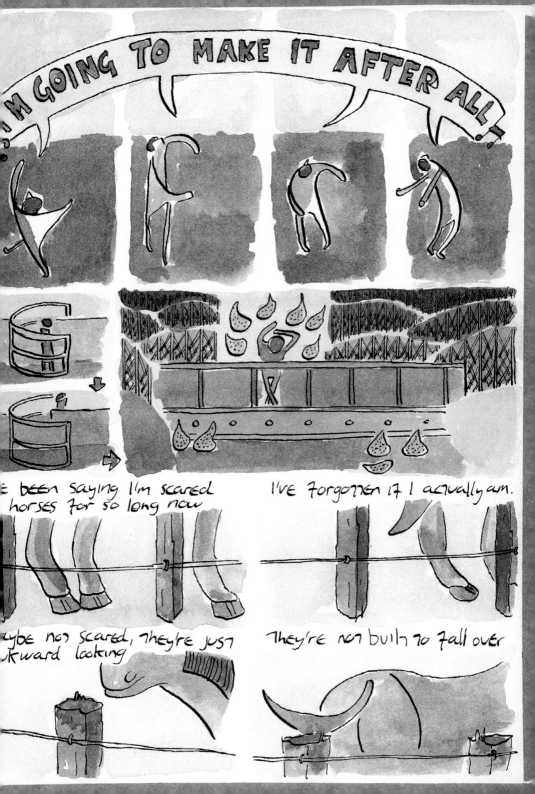

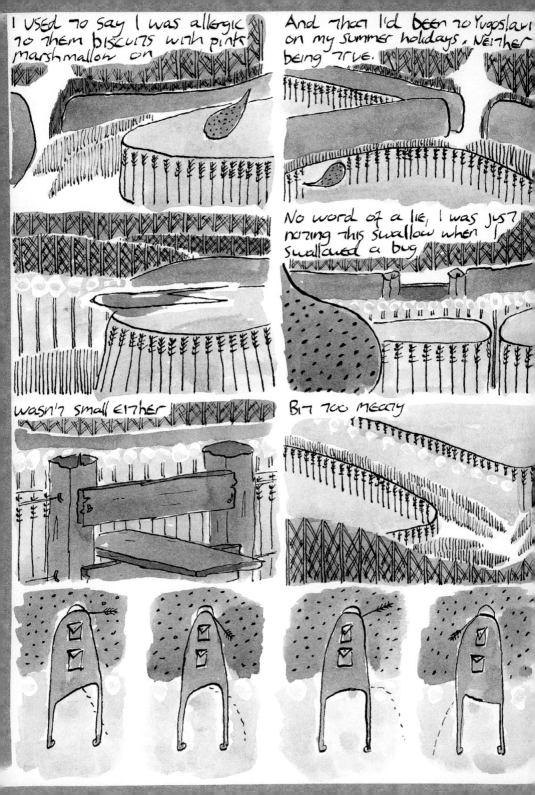

I USED TO SAY I WAS allergic to them BISCUITS with pink marshmallow on

And then I'd been to Yugoslavi on my summer holidays. Neither being true.

No word of a lie, I was just nozing this swallow when I swallowed a bug

wasn't small either

Bit too meaty

...ch Farm is less ...farm and more ...erton FC's training ...und

Either way it's past the footpath I'm looking for.

I should really have asked the guards on the gate for directions

...they were busy ...d I'd built it up ...my head.

I double back and find it anyway

Halewood Station's as basic a station as you can get really

and the driver looks at me funny when I don't run for his train

But I don't mind

chance for a sit down.

Hunts Cross Station's bridge seems a little oversized for a small station

But it has an amusing bounce to it which keeps me amused for ~~minutes~~ minutes

By my reckoning it takes just over an hour to get across two pages of an AtoZ

It's taken three hours to get to Hunts Cross

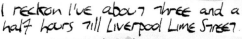

It's 10am now

I reckon I've about three and a half hours till Liverpool Lime Street

Fortunately there seems to be activity in Allerton Cemetery, with a mound of ~~earth~~ dirt and that cloth that looks like grass but 't. It's cloth.

I thought my AtoZ was relatively new but Allerton Station is no longer

It's been replaced by the Terrifying Liverpool South Parkway all gunship grey and piped music

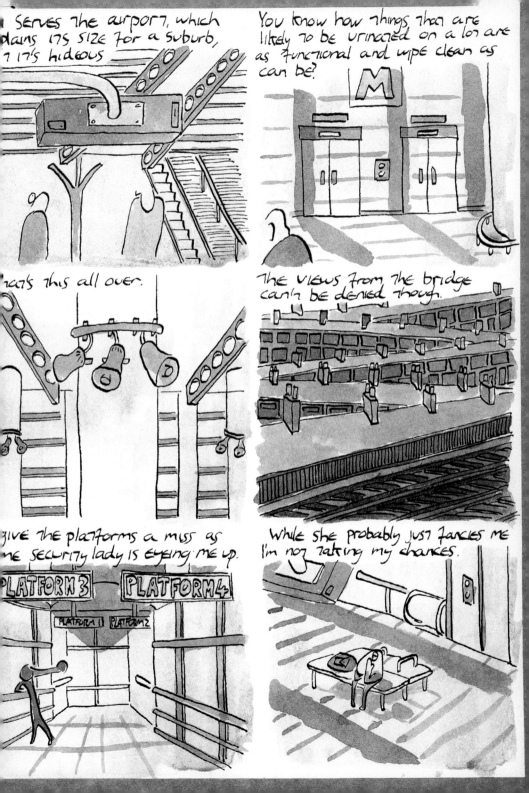

ossley Hill station's another remarkable but peaceful station.

Although its bridge looks like a human size sheep dip or cattle run of some kind.

y feet are screaming blue murder my caffeine infused enthusiasm ows no bounds.

The stations are coming thick and fast now. I might have to slow down a tad but I'm raring to go.

old on.....shit

I really am going to have to slow down as I've got less stations left than I thought.

Sure if I went into some d Bull induced trance but I've ly two stations left including e last one

MOSSLEY HILL   LA FITN

I'm not really ready for this to be over yet.

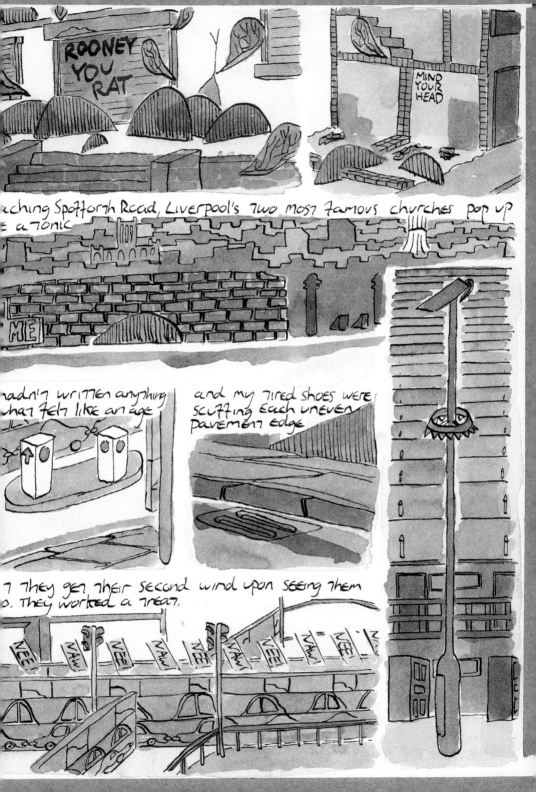

Edge Hill Station surprises me with its understated grandeur in less than sexy settings

From its walled and cobbled approach

To the two barely utilised buildings

Great clock as well

Which says I've 55 minutes to make my prediction true

I'm not rushing any more though

I want to do Liverpool the justice it deserves

I'm on the last page of my A to Z now

Not just that, the last three squares

JRCH OF ENGLAN HIGH SCHOOL

I begin furiously taking notes

HBISHOP CHU BLANCH HIG

Caffeine ran out long ago. Now I'm just panicking about this ending. Shit, I'm outside another school!

Someone arrest me!

Take me in!

NEE! NAW!

Drag this thing out a bit longer.

I'm noting everything mo

Uni.

Guy in shorts.

Some poet looking guy

Cathedral's clo

My brain freezes and my
mouth dries up

I've forgotten how tired
and sore I am now

I'm just running out of Liverpool now,
running out of tracks

I anticipated being pleased to see Liverpool Lime Street Station

Not so apparently

For the record I'm 10 minutes ahead of my ETA

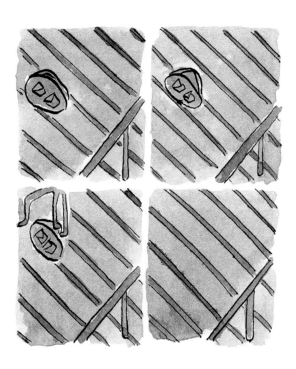

Oliver started self-publishing in '05 with the House Of Fire trilogy before moving on to produce the first five Trains Are...Mint. As fun as that was, he's glad someone else is taking the financial hit for now. He checks his email like every five minutes or something stupid like that so he'd be beside himself if he actually got one now and then at olivereast@hotmail.com

He lives and works in Manchester, UK, with his two cats and his Clare.

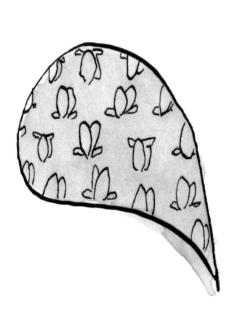

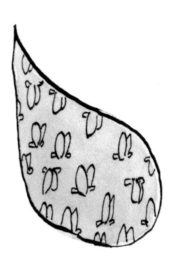